the A

DeZANiTiZED

Adapted by Suzanne Lord
Based on a television script by Paul Rugg

READING

SCHOLASTIC INC.
New York   Toronto   London   Auckland   Sydney

Cover illustration: Erik Doescher
Drawings by Animated Arts
Art Direction and Design: Neuwirth & Associates, Inc.

ISBN 0-590-53529-3

12 11 10 9 8 7 6 5 4 3 2   6 7 8 9/9 0 1/0

Printed in the U.S.A.   40
First Scholastic Printing, September 1996

"COUCH TALK"

ONE DAY IN THE WARNER BROS. PSYCHIATRY BUILDING, A DEEPLY DISTURBED PERSON IS IN THE OFFICE OF DR. SCRATCHANSNIFF.

I ZUPPOSE IT VOULD BE VISE TO START AT ZAH VERY BEGINNING.

PATIENT NAME! SCRATCHI...

GO ON...

8

9

"UND ZEN, JUST RECENTLY..."

ZAME TIME NEXT VEEK, MR. EASTWOOD. I MUST TELL YOU, ZESE SESSIONS MAKE _MY_ DAY!

"IT HAPPENED...."

17

24

25

YES,
DR. SCRATCHANSNIFF?

GET ZESE KIDS
OUT OF HERE!

28

DEEEESGUSTING!

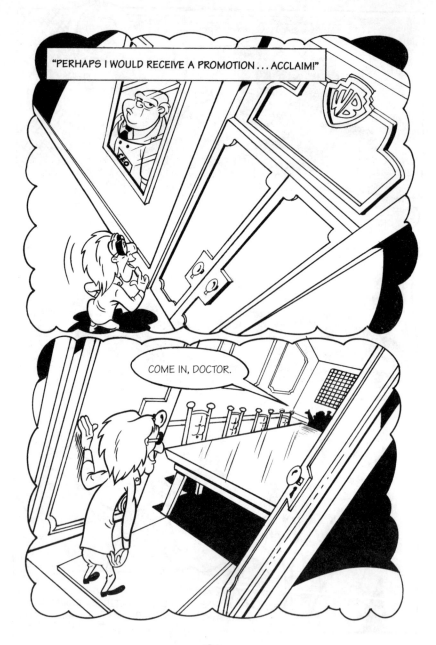

34

37

39

42

44

STOP VITH ZAH FENCE! ZERE IS NO FENCE!

GOOD. I'D RATHER HAVE SOME UMBRAGE, ANYWAY.

NEVER MIND ALL ZAT. I SINK IT'S TIME VE GOT DOWN TO BUSINESS.

55

"DOT TO DOT!"

"AFTER DAYS OF RESEARCH, I DECIDED TO MEET VITH EACH VARNER BROTHER INDIVIDUALLY."

I VOULD START VITH DER VARNER BROTHER — I MEAN, VARNER SISTER — I MEAN, VARNER BROTHER SISTER —

I VOULD START VITH **DOT!**

65

"GOING WAKKO!"

70

73

75

76

77

"ME AND MY YAKKO"